I, AUGUSTA

by ANGUS McGILL & DOMINIC POELSMA

BARRIE & JENKINS
COMMUNICA - EUROPA

First published in 1978 by
Barrie and Jenkins Ltd
24 Highbury Crescent, London N5 1RX

ISBN 0 214 20589 4

Printed in Great Britain by litho at
The Anchor Press Ltd, and bound by
Wm Brendon & Son Ltd
both of Tiptree, Essex

MAGNIFICENT!

SUBLIME!

AND WHAT ABOUT THE ONE WITH THE **MOUSTACHE**!

DARLINGS! QUELLE DIVINE HOLS! SIMPLY WHIZZING DOWN THE MOUNTAINS. SUCH FUN!

I'VE BOUGHT EVERYONE A LITTLE SOMETHING. THERE'S SOMETHING FOR YOU AND YOU AND YOU AND ALSO I'M HAPPY TO SAY A LITTLE SOMETHING …

FOR ME.